Great Expectations

Charles Dickens

Academic Industries, Inc.
West Haven, Connecticut 06516

ISBN 0-88301-751-2

Published by
Academic Industries, Inc.
The Academic Building
Saw Mill Road
West Haven, Connecticut 06516

Printed in the United States of America

about the author

The most popular, and perhaps the greatest of English novelists was Charles Dickens. Born in 1812, Dickens was the son of a clerk in the Navy-Pay office.

Although from a poor background, Dickens was both ambitious and industrious. His education came from books, those in school as well as his own. He wrote of people as he saw them and created some of the most timeless characters in literature.

The turning point in his life came at the time of his marriage. Both his wedding day and his first publication occurred in the same year. From that time, he continued to write many novels during the conventional Victorian era.

One of his most famous works is *A Tale of Two Cities*. This novel is a serious and sensational experiment in historical romance. It has a dual theme: love and death, and what effect they have on the novel's characters. On the other hand, *Great Expectations* is the story of a boy whose whole life is an uphill fight. In the end, however, Pip's goodness wins out over the forces that have always kept him down.

Charles Dickens

Great Expectations

Joe

Estella

Pip

Pip (older)

Magwitch

Miss Havisham

Young Philip Pirrip found his name hard to say—so he called himself Pip. As he sat in the churchyard thinking about it, a man rose from among the gravestones!

Speak quietly and tell me your name! Where's your mother? And where's your father?

My name's Pip, sir. My mother and father are both dead.

Who do you live with?

With my sister, Mrs. Joe Gargery. She's the wife of the blacksmith, sir.

I . . . I promise, sir.

Early tomorrow morning, bring me a file and some food. Don't say a word or I'll *kill* you!

As soon as the man let him go, Pip rushed home.

You're late! I was worried about you, Pip!

Come wash up, Pip, and we'll have supper.

When Joe and Mrs. Joe were not looking, Pip stuffed his bread and butter down his pant leg.

Suddenly a loud noise filled the air.

Was that the great guns, Joe?

Yes. A warning. Another convict has escaped from prison.

Who's firing, Mrs. Joe?

The Hulks—the prison ships across the marshes. Now, enough questions! Off to bed!

Pip was afraid of Mrs. Joe's temper, but he was more afraid of the convict. Early in the morning he went downstairs. Since it was Christmas morning, the cupboard was full of food.

I must get a file from Joe's tools.

On this cold, misty morning, Pip ran toward the river. Dashing up a hill, he saw a man who seemed to be asleep.

When Pip touched his shoulder, the man jumped up. It was not Pip's convict! Looking frightened, the man ran off into the mist.

Pip soon found the convict and gave him the food and the file.

Pork pie and brandy! Thank you.

I am glad you enjoy it. Aren't you going to share it with the other man?

What man? Where?

Over there. He was dressed like you.

First I'll file this iron off, then I'll catch him.

As the convict filed away, Pip ran off.

Mrs. Joe talked badly only to Joe and Pip. With other people around, her mood changed. Pip ate very little of his Christmas dinner, but Mrs. Joe hardly noticed.

Uncle Pumblechook has brought us wine. And I have a special surprise—a nice pork pie!

While Pip was wishing that he had never seen the convict, there was a knock at the door.

The pie—it's gone!

Excuse me, but we need the blacksmith. This lock does not work, and these handcuffs will be used soon.

11

The handcuffs were fixed. Later, Joe and Pip left with the soldiers. Nearing the river, they heard a voice calling, "Here, guards! Here!"

I'm sorry they caught them, Joe.

I'm sorry, too, Pip old chap.

He tried to murder me!

He's lying! I could have been free, but I caught him!

As the first prisoner was being rowed back out to the Hulks, the other convict stared at Pip for a moment, then spoke to the sergeant.

I want to say something. I took some food and some brandy, and a pie from the blacksmith's house.

Took? You mean that you stole it?

Don't worry. You were welcome to it.

The boat had returned. Without another look at Pip, the first convict left.

Pip's life quieted down again, but not for long. Mrs. Joe and Uncle Pumblechook came home from a shopping trip one day with important news.

Wait 'till you hear! Miss Havisham wants Pip to come and play at her house!

The Miss Havisham? How does she know Pip?

Uncle Pumblechook talked about Pip when he went to pay his rent.

We've got to get you cleaned up, Pip!

Do you mean that old lady who keeps her house all boarded up?

We mean the old lady who is *very rich!*

The next morning Uncle Pumblechook took Pip to Miss Havisham's house.

13

Is this Pip? Come in, boy. Not you, sir.

There was no light at all in the dark hall.

After you, Miss.

Don't be silly, boy. You go in alone.

Pip opened the door and saw a very strange sight. Miss Havisham was sitting at a table, as if getting ready for a wedding. But she was very old, and everything was yellowed with age.

Come closer, Pip. Do you know that I haven't seen the sun since before you were born? It's because my heart is broken.

Pip wondered if the clocks were broken too. They were all stopped at 8:40.

My sister says that I am to play here.

Go to the door and call Estella.

Play with this boy? Look at his rough hands and his thick boots!

Well, you can break his heart, can't you?

Pip walked around outside for a while. Then Estella brought him some food. Sadly, Pip remembered what Estella had said about his hands. He started to cry.

I'd like you to come by again in six days. What do you think of my ward?

She's very pretty. And very proud.

Good. I've hurt your feelings. Well, you can go home now.

Uncle Pumblechook and Mrs. Joe could hardly wait for Pip to tell them about Miss Havisham.

Well, how did it go, Pip?

Pretty well, sir.

Tell me about it, you stupid boy!

Now, Pip. Tell us what she's like.

Pip realized that Uncle Pumblechook had never seen Miss Havisham. He also guessed that they would not understand her strange house any more than he did. So he made up a wild story.

She had a beautiful coach in her room, but there were no horses. Estella, who is her niece, I think, went in with me. We served cake and wine on gold platters.

Can this be, Uncle?

Yes. I understand she is a little strange.

Pip felt bad about Joe's believing his story. He went over to the forge to tell the truth.

I lied about Miss Havisham's house.

Pip, old chap, that won't do. Why did you lie?

I don't know. I wish I weren't so common, Joe.

You're not. But lies won't help you, Pip. You need more schooling.

A lady named Miss Wopsle held classes for boys, but she spent most of the time asleep.

Biddy, you know more than Miss Wopsle. Will you help me learn?

That looks like a buckle.

That's a "D." You must practice drawing it. And then you must study these store prices.

Six days later, Pip returned to Miss Havisham's house.

Well, boy. What do you think of me today?

You are still pretty, but you're not as mean.

Much to Pip's surprise, Estella slapped his face.

They passed a man coming down from Miss Havisham's room.

This is a local boy.

Well! You behave yourself, boy!

Miss Havisham took Pip into a large room. Everything was covered with dust and mold and was falling to pieces. A large table was covered with black mold and spiders.

Do you know what that is? My wedding cake!

After talking to Miss Havisham for a long time, Pip was brought downstairs into the courtyard. When he looked through a window in an old garden house, Pip found another boy looking out.

Hello, young fellow! Come and fight.

While Pip stared in surprise, the boy came outside and took off his jacket and shirt.

Here. I'll give you a reason to fight.

Pip got angry, and soon the boy was on the ground with a black eye and a bloody nose.

Can I help you up?

No, thank you. Goodbye.

Meanwhile, Estella was waiting for Pip at the gate with the keys.

Come. You may kiss my cheek.

Pip did so happily.

Pip was afraid to return to Miss Havisham's house, but no one had said anything about the fight. The young boy was gone too.

Soon Pip's life settled into a routine.

Well, Pip. Don't you think Estella gets prettier every day?

Yes, ma'am.

Estella's moods changed so often that Pip did not know what to think.

You are a stupid boy.

That's right, Estella. Break his heart.

At the end of about eight months, Pip arrived home with a message.

Miss Havisham wants to see Joe and my apprentice papers.

Am I a doormat? A slave? Can't she ask me too?

It bothered Pip that Joe wouldn't speak directly to Miss Havisham.

I understand that Pip is to work for you, Mr. Gargery.

Pip, you know I want to teach you to be a blacksmith.

Pip has been a good boy, and he is finished here. Here is some money for him, but I won't be giving him any more.

I didn't ask Miss Havisham for any money—but thank her for me, Pip.

By the time they had reached Uncle Pumblechook's, Joe felt better.

Well, what did she give Pip?

Nothing. But Miss Havisham sent her best to you, Mrs. Joe Gargery. And she said to put this money into your hands. Right, Pip?

Pip was too surprised by Joe's words to say anything.

As the weeks went on, Pip worked hard for Joe, trying to make up for the secret shame he felt for his job and his home. One day Joe told Pip and Orlick, his helper, that they could have a half-day off from work.

Joe, you fool! Wasting pay on that lazybones!

You're a witch, Mrs. Gargery. A mean one!

Mrs. Joe screamed at Orlick, and Joe knocked him down. Pip was glad to leave, and he hurried to Miss Havisham's house.

Well! I hope you don't want anything.

No indeed, ma'am. I just want to tell you that I'm doing well in my work.

Do you miss Estella? She has gone to school in another country.

Miss Havisham soon told Pip that he had to leave. After that, he felt even more unhappy with his life.

Pip was late getting back home. He met Orlick on the way. A small crowd had gathered at the blacksmith's house.

Joe was out, but nobody took anything.

Mrs. Joe's been hit with a prisoner's leg iron.

Mrs. Joe was never the same again. She was not able to speak. Biddy came to take care of the house.

Biddy, I'm unhappy. I don't want to be a common person.

Miss Estella's words? Don't listen to her!

If she's so nasty, Pip, why do you want to see her?

I can't help myself. I love her.

Every year on his birthday Pip went to see Miss Havisham. Estella was still away.

Four years passed. Then a stranger found Joe and Pip. He was the same man Pip had passed on the stairs at Miss Havisham's house.

My name is Jaggers. I am a London lawyer. The news I have is that Mr. Pip is to be brought up as a gentleman in London.

The name of the person who is giving the money is to remain a secret. I will act as a guardian. Agreed?

Agreed.

I have some money to pay you for the loss of Mr. Pip's work.

No! Pip and I are friends. I don't want any money.

Mr. Jaggers' news made Pip feel strange. His dream of becoming a gentleman was soon to come true. But he suddenly felt lonely.

Will you help Joe with his learning?

No, Pip. Joe is happy for you—but he is a proud man.

He can come to see me, then. I will help him.

Joe will want to stay here, where he is well-liked.

Following Mr. Jaggers' orders, Pip bought some new clothes.

Only the best for a London gentleman!

Dear boy! Will you join me for a glass of wine?

When his new clothes were ready, Pip visited Miss Havisham's house once again.

I am so thankful for my good luck.

Mr. Jaggers has told me of it. Well, goodbye, Pip.

Pip left home early the next morning. He kissed his sister, Mrs. Joe, even though she still didn't understand anything. He hugged Joe and Biddy and set off in the London stagecoach.

In London, Pip found his new guardian very busy.

I have very little time, Mr. Pip. But you are to get an allowance. My clerk Wemmick will give it to you.

You may charge what you need at these places. Wemmick will take you to Barnard's Inn—to Mr. Pocket's rooms where you will sleep. Monday you will go to Hammersmith, his father's house.

Barnard's Inn was a group of flats in several old buildings. Most of them were for rent.

You want something? Oh, you want to shake hands?

I wish to thank you.

After quite a wait, Pip heard footsteps on the stairs.

Mr. Pip? Sorry I'm late. Please come in.

It's rather empty.

It will be fine.

You're the boy I saw at Miss Havisham's house.

And you are the boy who wanted to fight!

My father is Miss Havisham's cousin. I was there for a while—but it didn't work out.

Is Estella your cousin, too?

No. Miss Havisham just wanted Estella to live there. The old woman wanted her to break men's hearts.

For what?

Just then, their dinner was brought in from a nearby eating place.

I'll tell you the story after we've eaten this great meal—which you are paying for. Now, why were you at Miss Havisham's?

Pip told Herbert Pocket his story, adding the fact that he did not know his benefactor.

A favor, please. Will you correct my manners?

Gladly. In London we do not put the knife into the mouth. We use the fork.

Now for Miss Havisham's story. Her father was a brewer. When he died, he left her a large amount of money, as well as some to her half-brother.

Miss Havisham had been giving large sums of money to a man she was to marry. My father told her not to. Soon he was ordered out of the house.

The day of the wedding arrived. But instead of seeing the man she was to marry, Miss Havisham received a letter calling off the wedding.

It arrived at 8:40?

Right. She never went outside again. It was thought that the man and her half-brother planned to get her money.

Although nobody said it, both Herbert and Pip thought that Miss Havisham was the person paying for Pip's education.

Mr. Jaggers had made plans for Pip to study with Matthew Pocket, Herbert's father. Two other young men, Drummle and Startop, were also studying with him.

It's an odd house, but friendly. And father is very smart.

Mr. Pocket was a good teacher, and Pip studied hard. Evenings were often spent rowing a boat on the river.

Don't worry about Drummle. He hardly ever talks to anyone.

Would you mind if I kept my room at Barnard's Inn? I would like to buy some new furniture for the place.

Great!

Wemmick, Mr. Jaggers' clerk, was pleasant but businesslike when Pip asked him for his allowance. He surprised Pip when he invited him to his house.

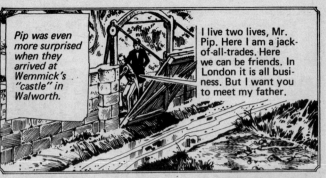

Pip was even more surprised when they arrived at Wemmick's "castle" in Walworth.

I live two lives, Mr. Pip. Here I am a jack-of-all-trades. Here we can be friends. In London it is all business. But I want you to meet my father.

Here's a friend of mine. Just nod your head, Mr. Pip. He's very deaf.

This is a fine place, sir, and welcome to it.

The gardens, the lake, the fountain—Mr. Jaggers must like it.

He's never seen it. Never heard of it. He's not a part of my life once I leave the office.

When Pip returned to London, he found a letter from Biddy. Joe was coming to London.

Pip, how are you, sir?

Oh, Joe. Don't call me "sir." Meet my friend, Herbert Pocket.

Herbert greeted Joe warmly.

I came to London with Mr. Wopsle. But I also came to tell you, Pip, that Miss Estella is home. Miss Havisham wants to see you.

Pip decided to go to see Miss Havisham the next day, but he wouldn't stay with Joe.

Orlick! You're not at work?

Ah, young master, there's changes. I'm the gatekeeper here now.

Did you recognize Estella?

Not at first. She is more of a lady, more beautiful!

Estella and Pip walked in the yard.

I have missed you.

Let me warn you, Pip. I have no heart.

When Pip was alone with Miss Havisham, she grabbed his arm tightly.

I adopted Estella so she would be loved, Pip. Ah, Mr. Jaggers. You are right on time.

Mr. Jaggers and Pip both spent the night at the local inn. Before Pip took the stagecoach to London the next morning, he talked to Mr. Jaggers about Orlick.

We think that it was Orlick who attacked my sister.

A bad man, eh? Very well. I'll fire him.

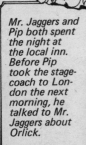

Pip returned to London. He felt bad about not seeing Joe, and he wondered how Estella really felt.

My sister has died. She will be buried next Monday. I must go home for a while.

Pip was still studying with Mr. Pocket. Herbert still worked in the customs house. And both spent more money than they had.

Dear Joe, how are you?

Pip, thank you for coming.

Pip spent the night in his old room. After a tearful goodbye to Joe and Biddy the next day, he headed back to London.

35

Mr. Jaggers sent for Pip on his twenty-first birthday.

Well, Mr. Pip. From now on you will get 500 pounds yearly—a large amount to take care of yourself.

Can you tell me who has been helping me?

When that person wishes to make himself known to you, I will be out of the picture. That is all I have to say.

On his way out, Pip spoke to Wemmick.

I have a friend I wish to help get ahead in business. Will you tell me how to do it?

You might just as well throw your money in the river! But I will help you anyway. Come to my home this evening.

When Pip arrived, Wemmick was not home, but his father had been watching for Pip.

John and Miss Skiffins walk every Sunday before tea. Ah, they're home. See how I can tell?

Pip laughed and nodded.

Miss Skiffins served tea. Mr. Wemmick's father read the paper out loud. Pip felt at home.

Later Pip again asked Wemmick's help for Herbert Pocket.

Herbert is not to know I'm behind this.

Right. I think I can help you. I'll let you know.

Through Wemmick, Pip paid out half of his money so that Herbert could work for a young merchant. Later, when Pip paid out more money, Herbert was to become a partner in the company.

37

Meanwhile, Estella had come to London to stay with an old friend of Miss Havisham. At plays, picnics, parties of all kinds, she used Pip to tease other young men.

I still have to write to Miss Havisham before I go to sleep.

To tell of the hearts you have won tonight? I'm sorry that Drummle was one.

He is stupid! He didn't know any better!

I trap many men, Pip. But I do not want to trap you.

A few days after the dance, Estella sent for Pip.

Miss Havisham wishes you to take me to her house. Will you?

Of course. We always obey Miss Havisham, don't we?

Once there, Miss Havisham and Estella had some bad words between them. Estella had taken her hand out of Miss Havisham's and had moved aside.

Are you tired of me? You have a cold heart. You are hard and thankless.

What do you want?

Love.

You took me as your own daughter. All I have is yours. But I have no love to give. I am as you have made me—without a heart.

When Pip and Estella began to play cards, all seemed as it had always been.

Herbert and Pip had moved into a better flat, but when Pip returned, Herbert had gone to France on business. So Pip was alone late one night when he heard a sound outside their door.

Are we alone?

Who are you to ask me that?

Dear Pip! You helped a stranger once, and he never forgot it.

You! Why you're Magwitch!

Pip was very afraid when he saw that the man was Magwitch, the man he had helped in the marshes long ago.

I was sent away for life. It will mean death if they catch me in England. So I call myself Provis.

But I had to see you, dear boy. Now, where do I sleep?

Pip gave Provis Herbert's room. The next day he bought Provis some new clothes to change his looks.

I've found you some rooms near here. I said you were my Uncle Provis. The watchman thought there was a man with you last night.

No, I came alone.

Soon after, Pip visited Mr. Jaggers.

You have learned from a Mr. Provis who your helper is?

Yes. Magwitch. I thought it was Miss Havisham.

You had no reason to think that. Now, remember, Magwitch is still in New South Wales. You've met a Mr. Provis. Good day, Mr. Pip.

Poor Herbert had the surprise of his life when he arrived home.

He's risking his life to be with you. You'll have to take him out of England.

Oh, Herbert. I don't like him! I cannot take any more of his money, but I have no job! And I cannot leave him.

Dear Pip and friend, my life has been hard. I've been in and out of jails. Remember the man I was fighting in the marshes? His name is Compeyson, and he is a bad one.

His partner Arthur died a crazy man. He kept yelling about a bride. Then I became Compeyson's partner in crime.

When we were caught, Compeyson talked against me, and got only seven years.

Miss Havisham's half-brother was Arthur. Compeyson was to marry her.

Since Compeyson might still be alive, Pip asked Herbert to watch Provis closely while Pip himself went to see Miss Havisham.

I know who my helper is. You led me to believe it was you, Miss Havisham.

Just to tease my family, Pip.

Your cousin Matthew and his son Herbert did not care whether you were teasing them or not. I need your secret help for Herbert.

Herbert doesn't know that I have been helping him in business. But things have changed and I can no longer do that.

I will think about it. Now, Estella, show Pip out. And tell him your news.

I am going to marry Bentley Drummle.

Oh, Estella! Not Drummle! I shall always love you.

Back in London, the watchman gave Pip a note from Wemmick. It read, "DON'T GO HOME."

Pip spent the night at an inn. In the morning he hurried to Walworth.

Compeyson is in London. Also, your house is being watched. I've told Mr. Herbert.

Where is Provis?

At Clara's, a friend of Mr. Herbert's. Visit him there tonight *before* you go home. You may be followed.

Clara and her father lived with a widow in a house near the river.

Please excuse me.

That great noise overhead is her father calling for his rum.

Provis was happily settled in the third floor bedroom.

For your safety I can't visit you again.

Then I'll carry messages for you. When the time comes, Pip and I will come by boat to get you.

Pip needed money badly. But he had sent an unopened purse back to Provis because he did not want to take any more from him.

Pip kept his boat. Sometimes alone, sometimes with Herbert, he went rowing.

All is well with Provis.

One evening after rowing, Pip had dinner with Mr. Jaggers and Wemmick.

Miss Havisham wants to see you, Pip.

I'll go tomorrow.

Once outside, Pip asked Wemmick about Mr. Jaggers' servant.

Molly? She was once in jail for murder. But Jaggers got her out, and she's been with him ever since.

Here is a letter for Mr. Jaggers. He will give you the money for Herbert. It will be our secret, Pip.

Oh, Pip. Forgive me.

I am not angry with you, Miss Havisham. But what of Estella?

Oh, what have I done to her? When Mr. Jaggers brought her here as a small child, he said, "I only wanted to save her from a sad life like mine."

Pip decided to take a walk outside before saying goodbye to Miss Havisham.

As Pip went back into the room, Miss Havisham came rushing toward him screaming. Her clothes were on fire!

With the help of the servants, the fire was put out, the doctor was sent for, and Miss Havisham was put to bed.

Pip's hands had been badly burned. Herbert took care of him.

Provis told me more of his life last night. He had a little daughter, but his wife told him the girl was dead. Then she murdered another woman. Jaggers was her lawyer.

Provis had gone away to help the case. He never found her again.

She is Jaggers' servant Molly. And Provis is Estella's father. But *that* must remain our secret.

On a Monday in March, Pip received a note from Wemmick. It said for Pip and Provis to leave England on Wednesday.

I have the passports. There is a ship, the *Hamburg*, leaving on Wednesday's high tide.

Startop will help me row while you steer. I'll tell Provis tonight to watch for us.

What's this? "Come ALONE to the marshes tonight at nine o'clock. It is about your Uncle Provis."

There's only a half-hour to catch the coach!

Upon entering the building near the marshes, Pip was caught in a noose and was tied to a wall ladder.

Orlick! What does this mean?

It means I'm going to kill you like I tried to kill Mrs. Joe. You made me lose my job with Miss Havisham!

I watched you in London. I know your Uncle Provis is Magwitch. I told my partner, Compeyson.

Orlick struck Pip, who yelled and kicked at him. The door burst open.

Forget Orlick. We need to get on with our business.

You dropped the note you received, Pip. Startop and I read it and were worried. We hired a coach and a guide. But Orlick ran away.

51

The plan was to meet the steamship far down the river. All started well. As Pip and Provis prepared to board the coming ship, a customs house galley pulled out from shore.

Everything went wrong. The galley pulled next to the smaller rowboat. The Hamburg passed close by, making huge waves. Provis reached over and pulled the cloak back from the galley passenger. It was Compeyson.

Pip, Herbert, and Startop were yanked into the galley as it pulled out of danger. Pip's boat had sunk. The two prisoners had gone overboard.

Soon after, Provis was rescued—and arrested as Magwitch. Pip was allowed to return to London with him.

I'm happy, Pip. I've seen you become a gentleman, and you'll have more money. But gentlemen and prisoners don't mix.

I've grown to like you too much to leave you!

When Pip hired Jaggers to defend Magwitch, he said there was no hope.

Compeyson's body was found. In his pockets were lists of Magwitch's land and money, but it will all go to the crown.

He must never learn that I cannot inherit from him.

Upon returning home, Pip found Herbert upset.

I'm off to Egypt to open our new office. If only you could join me!

Perhaps someday. I will miss you!

After seeing Herbert off, Pip found Wemmick waiting for him.

On Monday I plan to take a holiday. I want to go for a walk with you.

Are we going fishing?

No, but people will think so.

As they walked along, Pip became more and more puzzled by Wemmick.

Here's a church! Let's go in!

Here's some gloves! Let's put them on!

Here's Miss Skiffins! Let's have a wedding!

And so Wemmick and Miss Skiffins were married, with Pip acting as best man!

Meanwhile, Magwitch had been tried in court, and was found guilty of returning to England. Thirty-one other prisoners went to court at the same time.

You must get ready to die.

Sir, I am already sick, and I will die of that before the court can kill me.

Pip was allowed to visit Magwitch every day in the prison hospital. The man was in great pain, but he never said anything about it.

Dear friend, you once told us you had a child you loved and lost. She is alive. She is now a beautiful lady, and I love her.

Slowly Magwitch raised Pip's hand to his lips, smiled, and died.

The fight with Orlick, the worry of trying to help Magwitch, and the worry of owing so much money finally hit Pip. He became very sick.

Mr. Pip, we have to take you to jail because of your bills. You must come with us.

I would if I could. But I cannot even lift my head.

Let's get out of here!

Ah, you're awake at last! No, I'm not a ghost. It's me, Joe.

How long have you been here?

Why, for weeks! Wemmick sent me a note. And Biddy said, "Go to him quickly, Joe." And so I came.

How is Miss Havisham?

She died soon after the fire. Left everything to Miss Estella—except some money to Matthew Pocket. "Because of Pip," she wrote.

Orlick's in jail. He robbed old Pumblechook and got caught.

Under Joe's tender care, Pip soon got better.

I am glad I was sick, Joe. It has given me good times with you that I shall never forget.

We were always good friends, you and me.

The next morning Pip found a note from Joe. He had gone home. There was also something saying that Joe had paid his overdue bills.

A few days later, Pip went to see Joe and Biddy.

Biddy, you look wonderful! Joe, how smart you look!

It's my wedding day! I am married to Joe!

Biddy, you have the best husband in the world. And Joe, you have the best wife. Now for my news.

I am going to join Herbert Pocket in Egypt. I will work and return the money you spent on me, Joe. You mean so much to me.

Nothing needs to be said between friends, Pip, old chap.

Pip went to Egypt and worked hard for Herbert. He paid all his other bills. After many years he became a partner in the company. Clara's father died, so she and Herbert were married.

I came here to tell you both how pleased I am with this office. But, Pip, I could no longer stay quiet. I have told Herbert that it was you who helped him get his start.

Pip, dear friend. I don't know what to say.

Clara tells me it is time you had a holiday in London.

Yes, I would love to see Joe and Biddy again.

It had been eleven years since Pip had seen them.

When Pip opened the Gargery kitchen door, he felt he was seeing himself as a child.

We gave him the name of Pip.

And we hope he is just like you.

You should get married, Pip. Do you still think of Estella?

Yes. Two years ago her husband treated a horse badly, and it killed him. I heard he treated Estella badly, too. She may have married again.

Toward evening, Pip decided to have a last look at Miss Havisham's house. The buildings had been torn down. Only the stone wall was left, with the gate open.

Estella! How strange to see you here where we first met.

This is all I have left from my unhappy life. I wanted a last look at it.

I have thought of you often. Do you still work in Egypt? Are you doing well?

Yes, I am doing well. And you have always kept your place in my heart.

Pain has taught me what a heart is. I hope we can part as friends, Pip.

Dear Estella! I do not think we will part this time. I want you to marry me!

THE END

61

COMPLETE LIST OF POCKET CLASSICS AVAILABLE

CLASSICS

COMPLETE LIST OF POCKET CLASSICS AVAILABLE
(cont'd)